FOR-GET ME NOT

By Gabriel M. Howell

Forget Me Not
First Edition (c) 2022 Gabriel Howell

Printed in China
ISBN-13: 978-8-9855863-0-5
SA 049
Library of Congress Control Number: 9798985586305

Published by Secret Acres
1717 E Vista Chino, A#13. A 7-832
Palm Springs, CA 92262

SECRET
ACRES

STARRING

complications

HEARTACHE

REBELLION

commitment

now my wrists
are labeled with
hard lessons

seven minutes in heaven
with them staring through the
cracks giggling calloused me

take it out on page

Hard work, heavy heart!
It feels so unexplainably
natural showing what
I'm capable of

Who could have predicted
vulnerability would come back
to bite me in the ass

Just talking
it out is for
functioning
people

Frustrating
is an
understatement
when you don't
understand
so I
present you
a picture

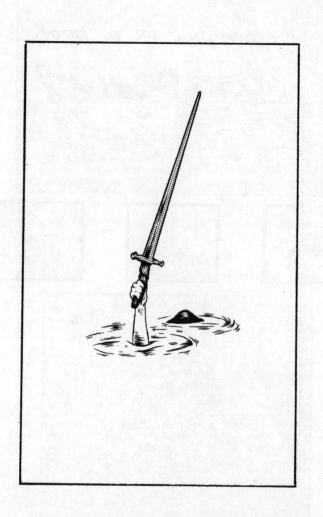

tortured Artist,
terrible beauty,

Seems to never go out of style

Are we all needing
something rotten to
digest for content
to feed others?
Sounds so glamorous,
Sign me up

I Guess there is a wisdom achieved through suffering

Good tales to tell about fucking up too much in your early 20's

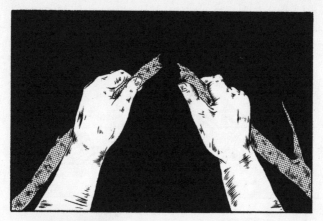

agree that visibility is an
enemy & still suffer from under exposure

Take
your tears
and travel
some place better

TO HELP EACHOTHER OUT

find a place where your soul & work ethic can fight for custody of your hands safely

to find
a way to
provide
off a
passion

I CAN'T LOCATE THE ESCAPE ROUTE

KEEP OUT!!!
(But PLEASE stay posted)

curating my corner of the world for public eye

Keeping up apperances

I'm not an algorithm, I'll fucking stab you.

the missing dose of lithium?

misinterpreting attraction for
love is the special of the night

Honey, I shrunk my self-esteem

tried owning insecurity
like a risky fashion
choice, but everyone sees
right through it

it's what's on the
insides that
counts, right?

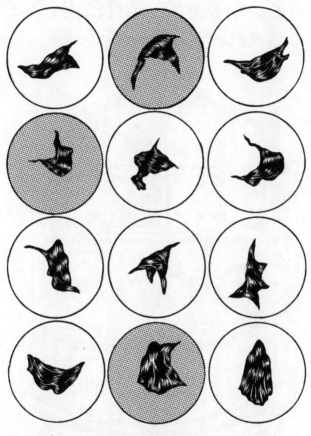

there's an entity craving
empathy that wants to be known

Constantly surveilled & never felt so alone

Makes a good starter home
for sensitives filled with malice

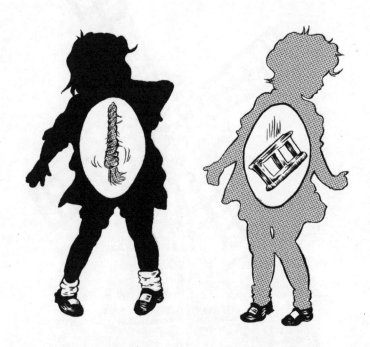

"Don't let it get to you"...

shakey handed decisions I struggle trusting myself

following to learn to imitate being normal

Icare.

Share Me softly
or
Square Up

Like my fists throwing punches in a dream I fall flat.

DEVASTATED;

My Demons look Different

THANKS
NOEL, LEON & THE SA CREW,
WINONA, CAROLINE, MAX
JESSICA, SEB, CARTA
NAYEF, & MY WIFE FOR
HELPING ME THROUGH
THE LONLINESS & SELF DOUBT
THAT COMES WITH MAKING
COMICS